primary 1997–1999 england

Works by the same artist

Presence

Deep

Special thanks to

Dawn Peters

Mohammed Ayub Khan

Amanda Ball

Claire Doherty

Natasha Howes

Debbie Kermode

Louise Connell

Fareda Khan

Mark Sealy

Exhibition supported by

IKON GALLERY

The Harris Museum &
Art Gallery, Preston

Published by Autograph ABP
www.autograph-abp.co.uk

© 2000 Clement Cooper

ISBN 1 899282 60 2

Design and production
EDT, London 020 8748 9565

Printing
P J Print Group

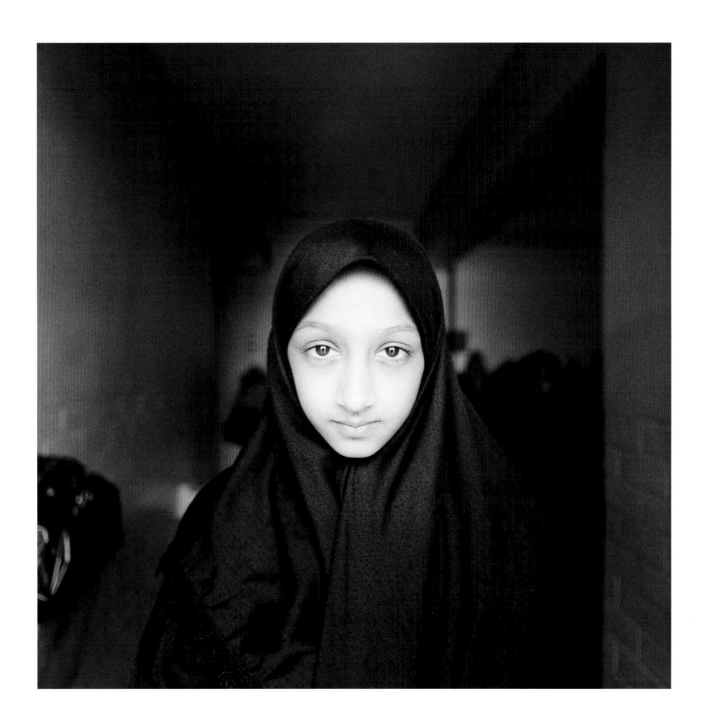